love songs

Production: Sadie Cook

Design and Typesetting by Xheight Limited
Published 1995

CAN'T STAY AWAY FROM YOU

Words and Music by
GLORIA ESTEFAN

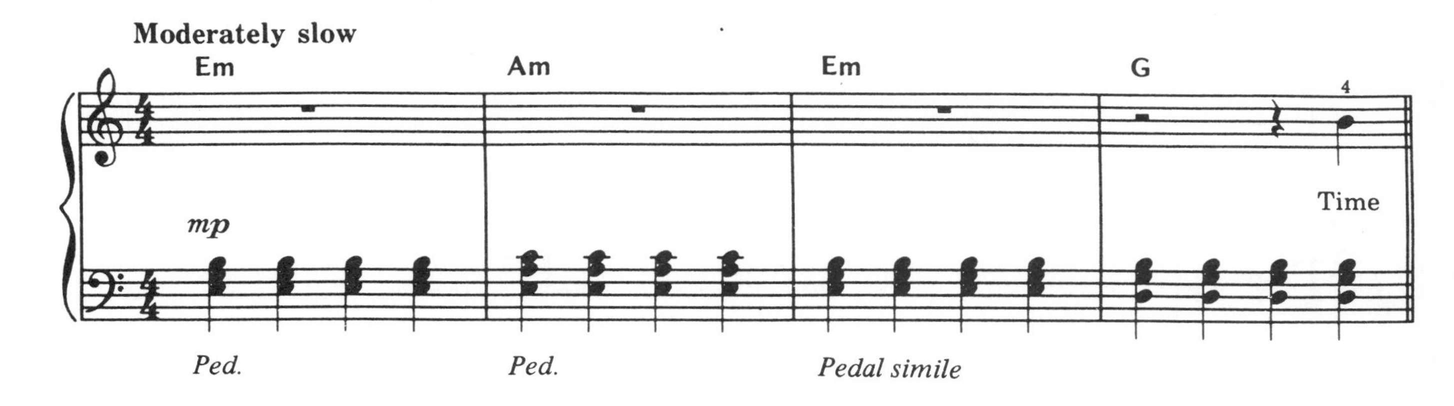

Em
G
don't wanna be just your
friend.
You keep tell-ing me that you're
Fmaj7
Gsus
not in love;
you want to throw it all a - way.
Chorus:
G
Fmaj7
G9
But I can't stay a - way from
you,
mf
I don't want to let you
C
Fmaj7
go.
Though it's kill - ing me,
that's true,
G7sus
G
there's just some things I can't con - trol.
Your love is slip-ping through my

Verse 2:
Hold on to every bit of hope, that's all I ever do;
Hoping you might change your mind and call me up to say
How much you need me too;
Though you're leaving me no other choice
Than to turn and walk away,
Look over your shoulder, I'll be there,
You can count on me to stay.
'Cause I can't stay away from you,
(To Chorus:)

ALWAYS

Words and Music by JOHN LEWIS,
DAVID LEWIS and WAYNE LEWIS

Cm7 A♭maj9 D9 C/D C/E D/F♯
ev - er it will be you and me. dim
cresc.
f
G D/G Dm/G C Am7
mp
Ooh, you're like the sun chas-ing all the rain a - way._ When you come a-round you bring
Am7/D G D/G G7 C
bright - er days. You're the per-fect one for me, and you for-ev-er will be; and
Am7 Am7/D G D/G
I will love you so for al - ways.
p espressivo
Dm7/G C(2) G/B Am7 C/D G(2)
mp rit.
p
Ped.
Ped.
*

AUTUMN LEAVES
(LES FUILELES MORTES)

English Words by JOHNNY MERCER
French Words by JACQUES PREVERT
Additional Verse Lyric by GEOFFREY PARSONS
Music by JOSEPH KOSMA

Em
B
hold. Since you went a - way the days grow
Em
D
D7
long, and soon I'll hear old win - ter's
G
F♯dim
B
f
song, but I miss you most of all my
Em
A/C♯
Am/C
B
dar - ling, when au - tumn leaves start to
1.
Em
fall. The fall - ing
2.
rit.
Em

CLOSE TO YOU (THEY LONG TO BE)

Words by HAL DAVID
Music by BURT BACHARACH

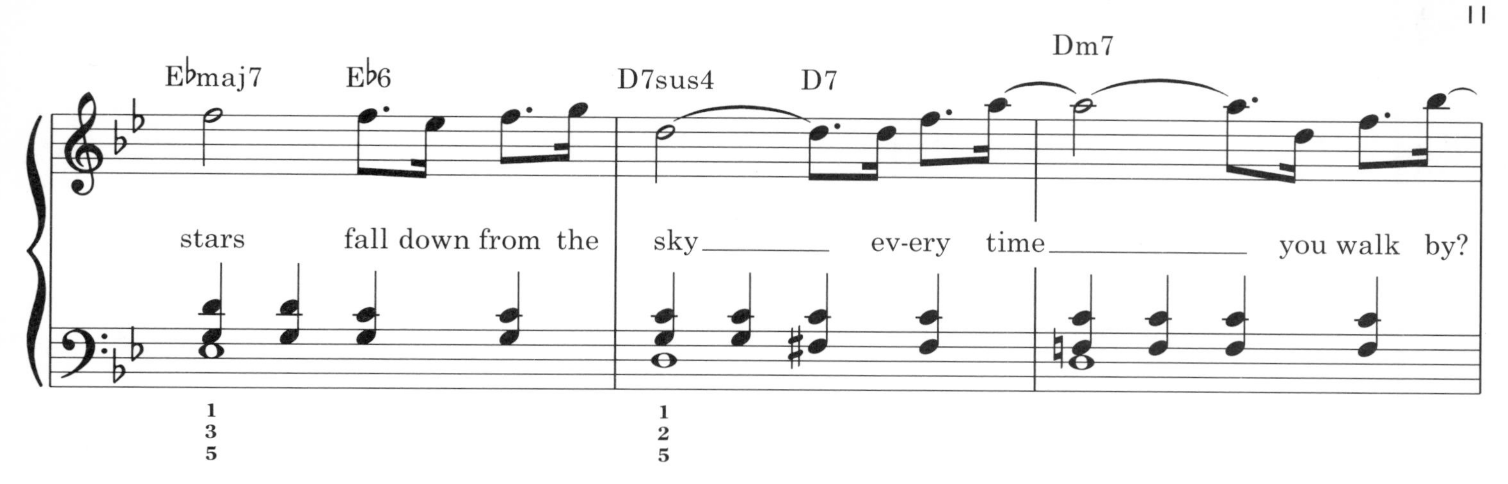
E♭maj7 E♭6 D7sus4 D7 Dm7
stars fall down from the sky ev-ery time you walk by?

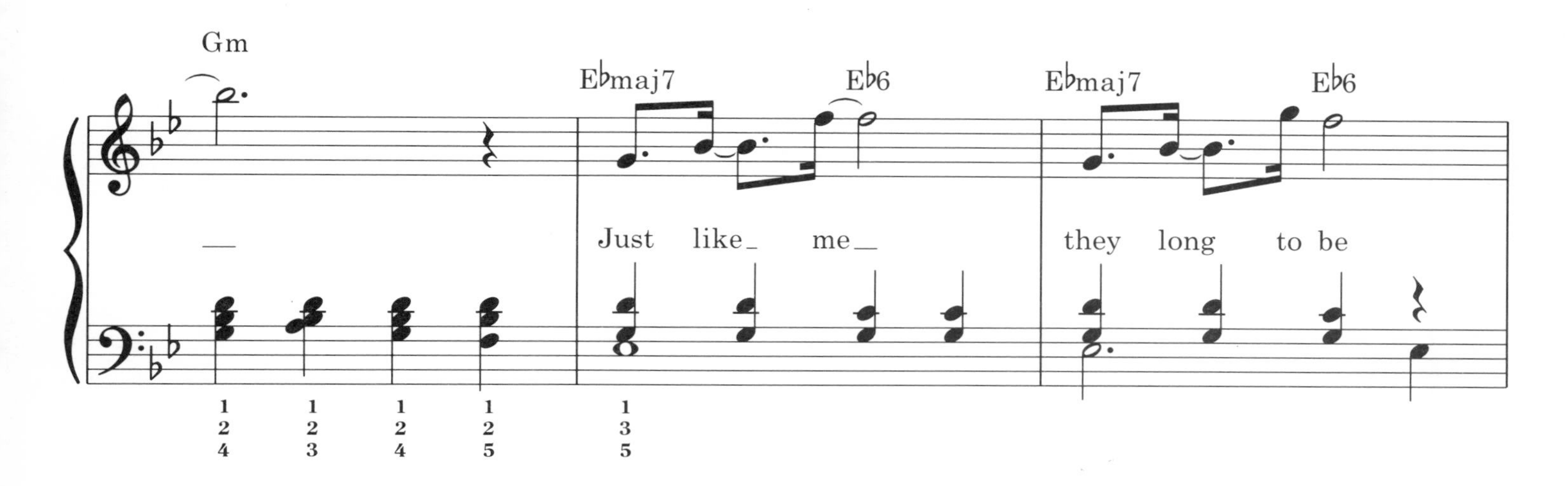
Gm E♭maj7 E♭6 E♭maj7 E♭6
Just like me they long to be

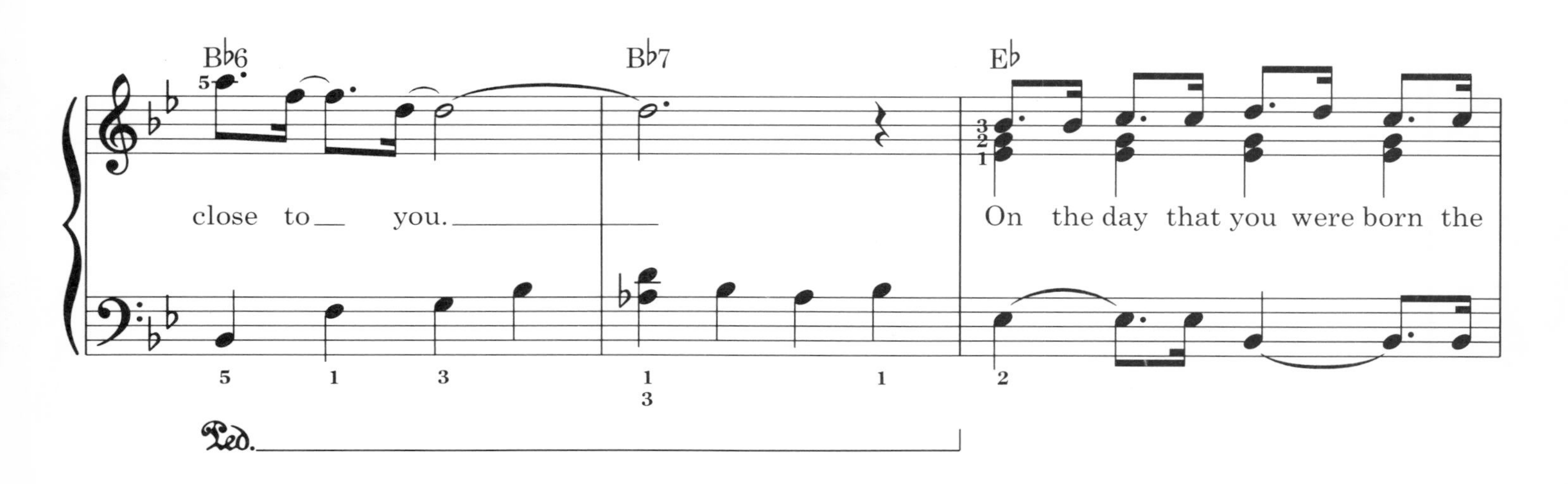
B♭6 B♭7 E♭
close to you.
On the day that you were born the
Ped.

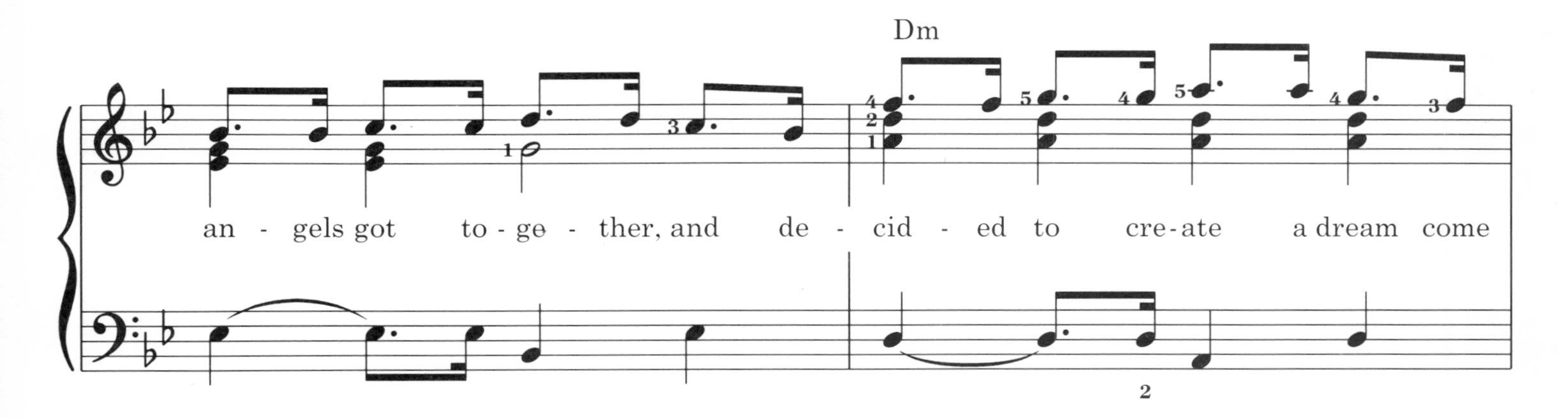
Dm
an - gels got to - ge - ther, and de - cid - ed to cre-ate a dream come

G7sus4
G7
true, so they
E♭
sprin - kled star - dust in your hair of
E♭maj7
E♭6
gold, and star - light in your eyes of
F
blue.
N.C.
That is
E♭maj7
E♭6
why all the boys in
D7sus4
D7
town fol-low you
Dm7
Gm
all a - round.
E♭maj7
E♭6
Just like me
E♭maj7
E♭6
they long to be
B♭6
close to you.

ENDLESS LOVE

Words and Music by
LIONEL RICHIE

Moderately slow

C
mp

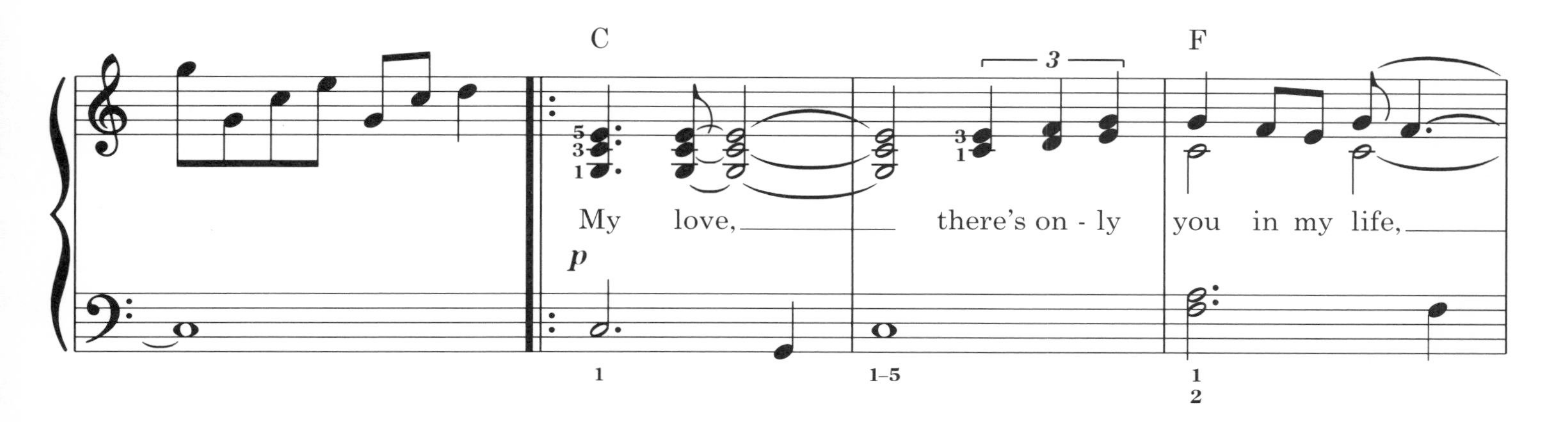
C
F
My love, there's on - ly you in my life,
p

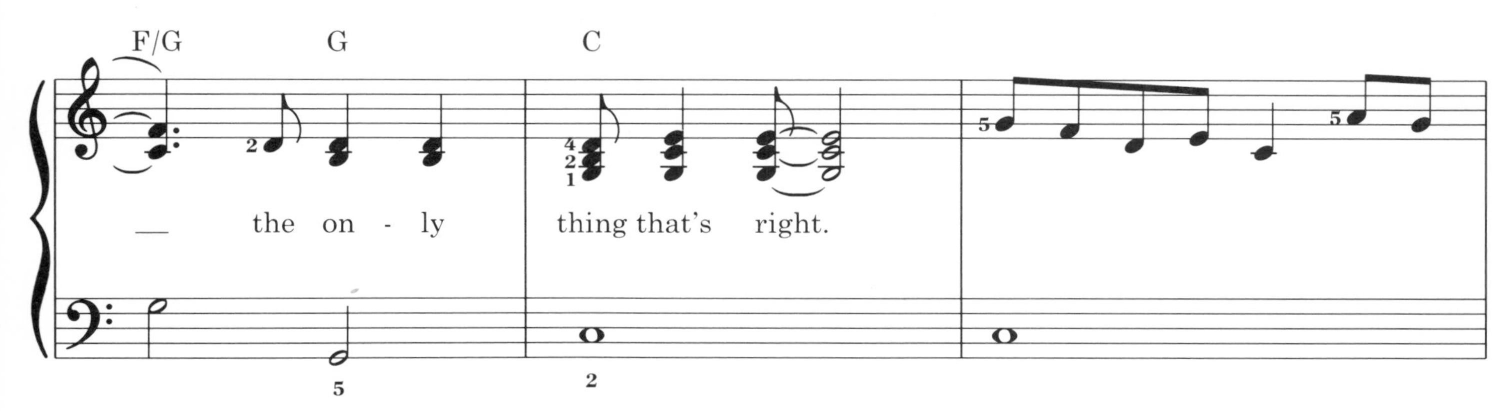
F/G
G
C
the on - ly thing that's right.

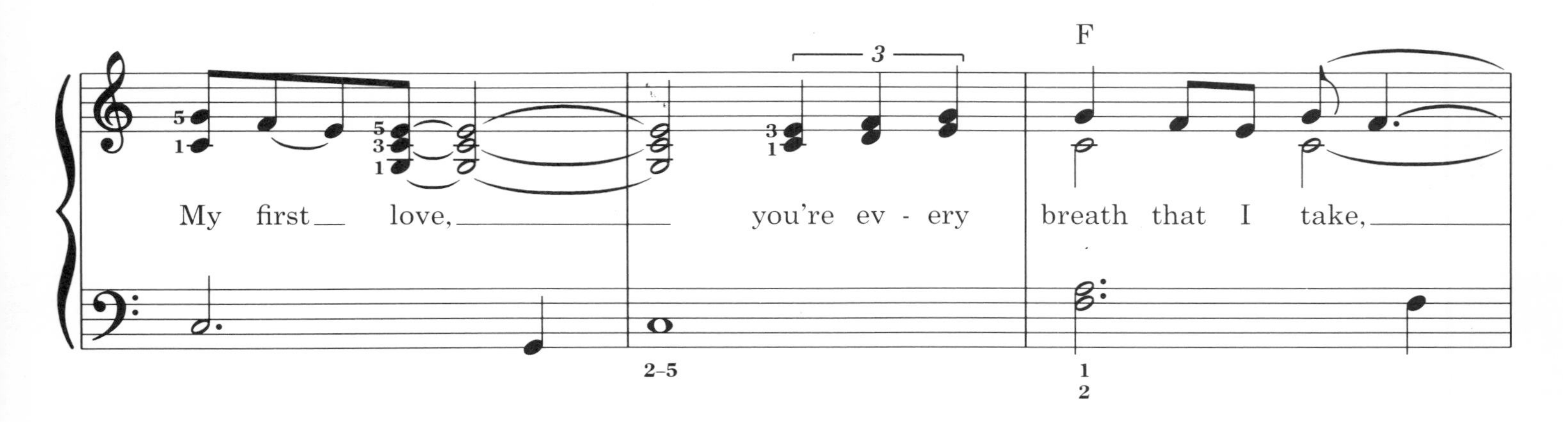
F
My first love, you're ev - ery breath that I take,

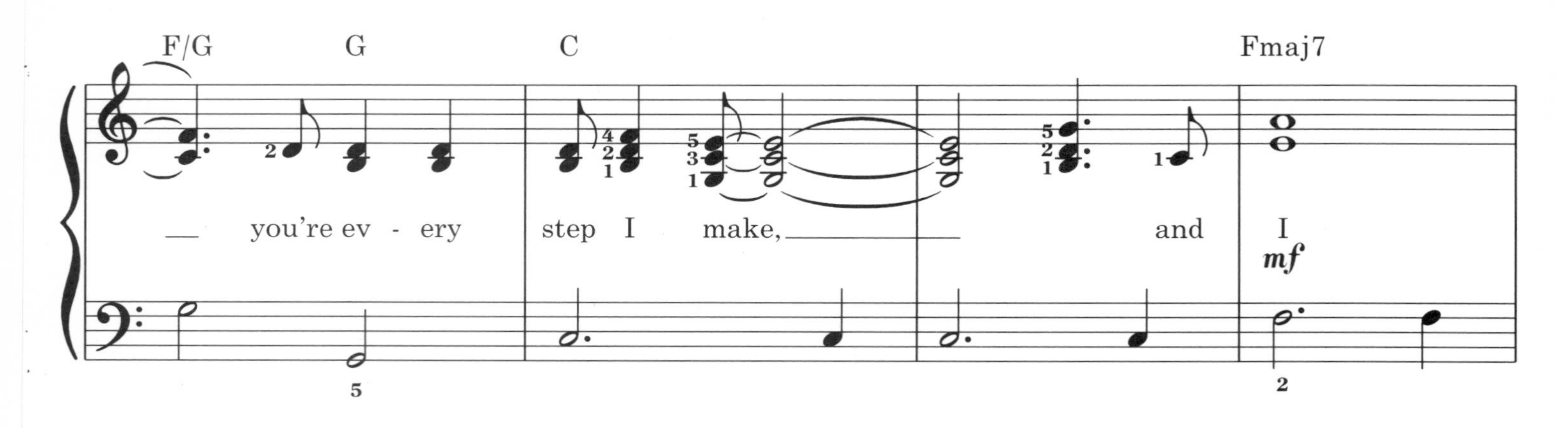
F/G
G
C
Fmaj7
you're ev - ery
step I make,
and I
mf

G9sus4
G
C
G/B
Am7
G
Fmaj7
I'd want to
share all my
love
with you,

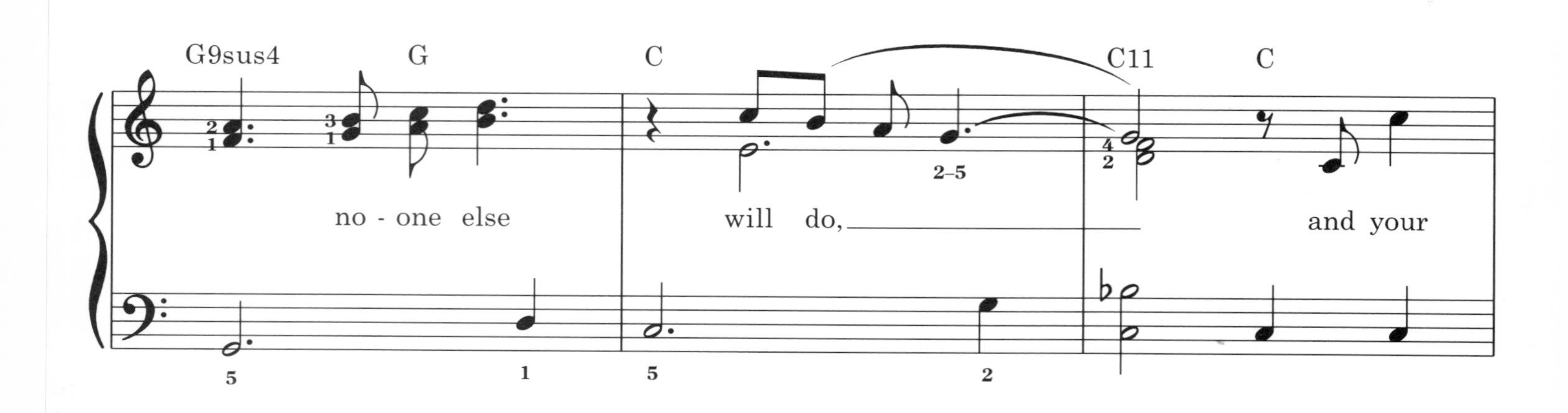
G9sus4
G
C
C11
C
no - one else
will do,
and your

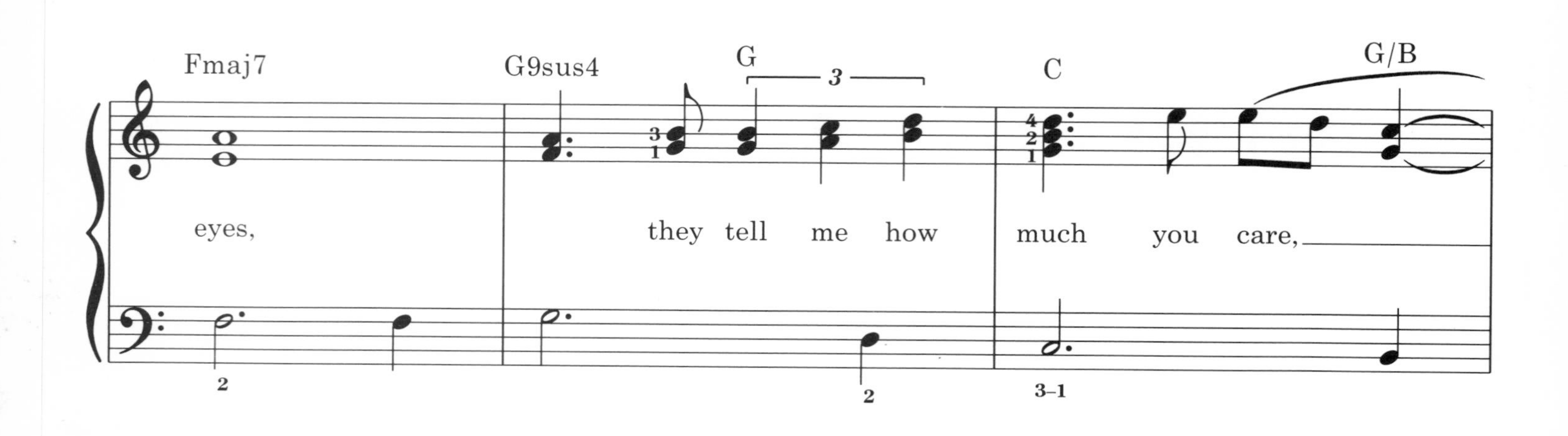
Fmaj7
G9sus4
G
C
G/B
eyes,
they tell me how
much you care,

1.
Am7
G
Fmaj7
Em7
Dm7
oh
yes,
you will
al - ways
be
G11
3
C
my
end - less
love.
2.
Am7
G
Fmaj7
Em7
Fmaj7
Oh
no,
I can't de - ny
this
love
I have in -
C/E
Fmaj7
C/E
- side,
and I'll
give
it all to
you
my
Dm
G11
C
love,
my
end - less
love.
p

THE FIRST TIME EVER I SAW YOUR FACE

Words and Music by
EWAN MacCOLL

Verse 2:
And the first time ever I kissed your mouth,
I felt the earth move in my hand,
Like the trembling heart of a captive bird
That was there at my command, my love.

Verse 3:
And the first time ever I lay with you,
And felt your heart so close to mine,
I know our joy would fill the earth
And last till the end of time, my love.

GOODBYE GIRL

Words and Music by
DAVID GATES

Cm
Gm7
Fm7
words you've heard_ be - fore. But, dar - ling, you ___ must
help - ing you ___ to see that I was meant_ for
Gm7
Bb11
with a beat
Bb9
trust them just_ once more. 'Cause, ba - by, good -
you and you_ for me. So re - mem - ber, good -
Eb
Gm7
Ab
Bb
Bb9
bye does - n't mean_ for - ev - er. Let me tell you, good -
bye does - n't mean_ for - ev - er. Let me tell you, good -
mf
Eb
Gm7
Ab
Bb
bye does - n't mean_ we'll nev - er be to - geth - er a - gain._
bye does - n't mean_ we'll nev - er be to - geth - er a - gain._

Cm
Gm7
Ab maj7
Db9
If you wake up and I'm not there_I won't be long_ a - way.___ 'Cause the
Though we may be so far a - part,_you still will have_ my heart.___ So for -
mp
Cm7
F9
1.
Bb11
Eb
things you do,__ my good - bye girl,__ will bring_me back to you.
get your past,__ my good - bye girl,__ 'cause
dim.
legato
Gm7/D
Ab
Bb7
2.
Bb11
now you're_home at __
Eb
Gm7/D
Ab
Bb7
Eb
last. ___
dim.
legato
molto rit.
pp

THE POWER OF LOVE

Words by JENNIFER RUSH and MARY SUSAN APPLEGATE
Music by CANDY DE ROUGE and GUNTHER MENDE

C/E
G
I could not for - sake, 'cause I am your la -
al - ways by your side,
f
C
- dy, and you are my man.
F
Dm
When-ev - er you reach for me, I'd do all that I can,
G
1.
2.3.
ev - en though there may be
we're head - ing for
C
F
some - thing, some-where I've ne - ver been.

D
C
Sometimes I am fright - ened, but I'm rea - dy to learn,
G
F
C
Fine
'bout the pow - er of love.
F
G
C
F
G
mf
The sound of your heart beat - ing,
made it clear sud-den -
Am
F
G
C
- ly,
the feel - ing that I can't go on
F
G
D.𝄋 al Fine
is light years a - way,
'cause I am your la -
f

I'LL BE THERE

Words and Music by BERRY GORDY, HAL DAVIES,
WILLIE HUTCH and BOB WEST

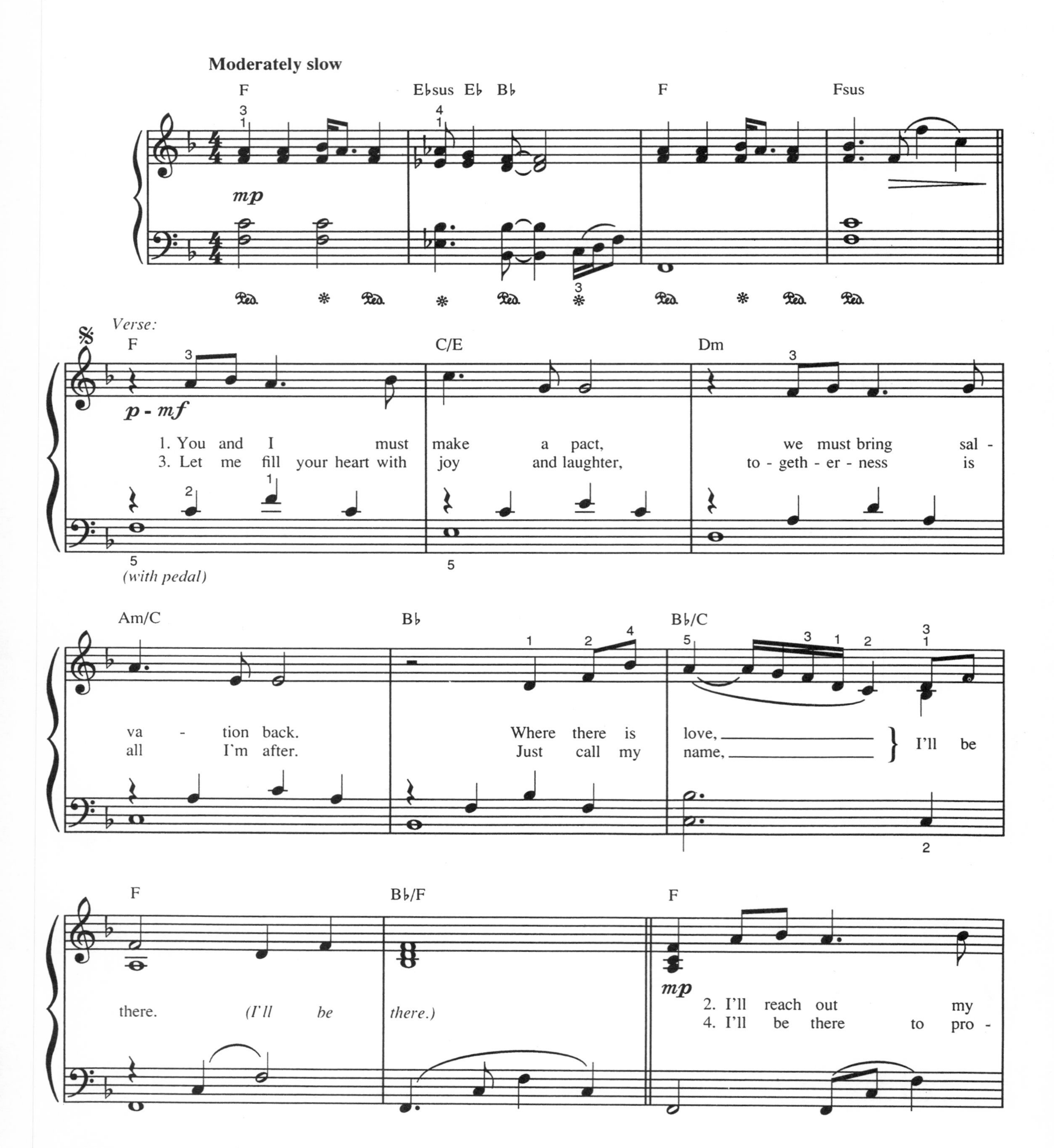

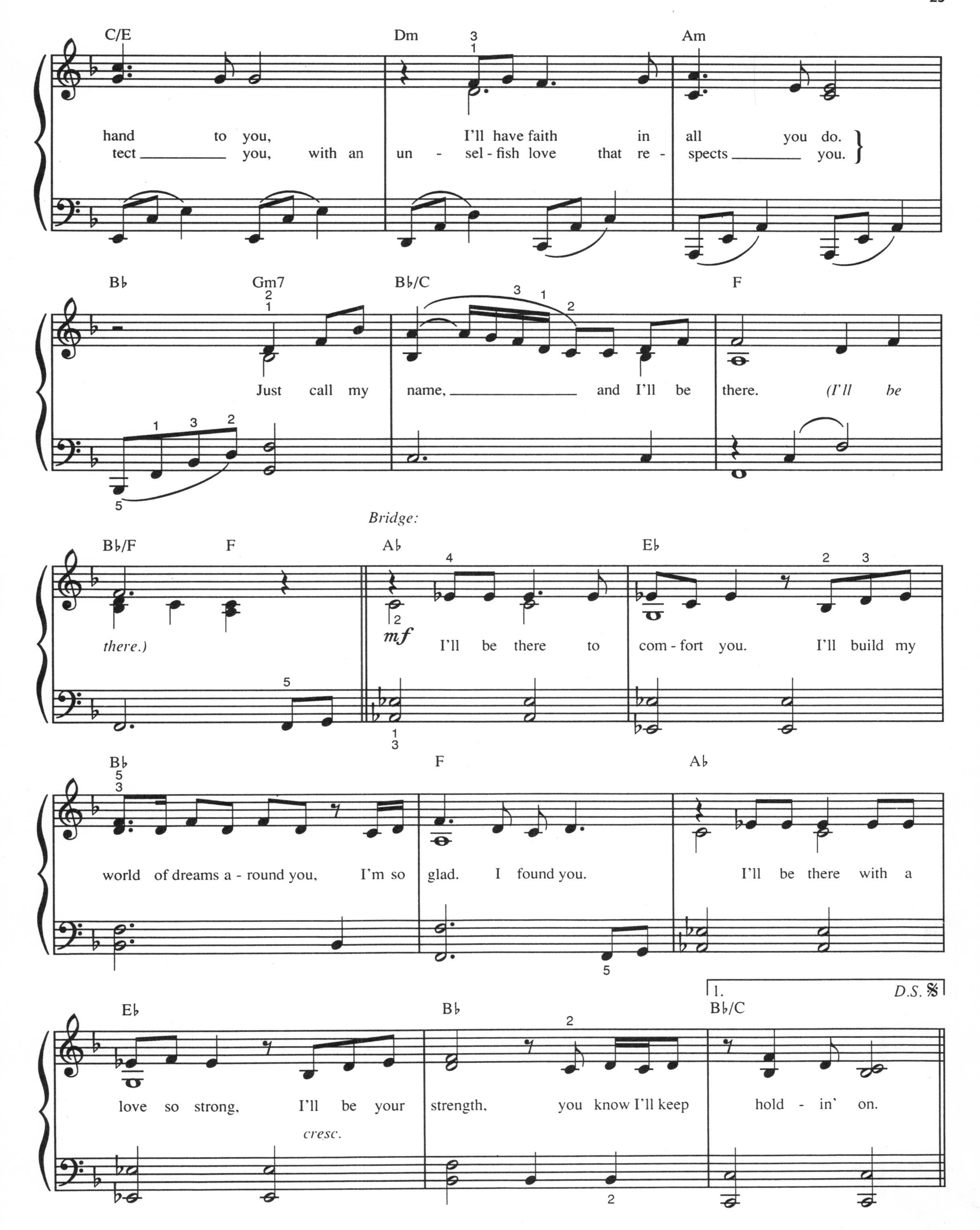
C/E
Dm
Am
hand to you, I'll have faith in all you do.
tect you, with an un - sel - fish love that re - spects you.
B♭
Gm7
B♭/C
F
Just call my name, and I'll be there.
(I'll be there.)
B♭/F
F
Bridge:
A♭
E♭
mf
I'll be there to com - fort you. I'll build my
B♭
F
A♭
world of dreams a - round you, I'm so glad. I found you.
I'll be there with a
E♭
B♭
1.
D.S.
B♭/C
love so strong, I'll be your strength, you know I'll keep hold - in' on.
cresc.

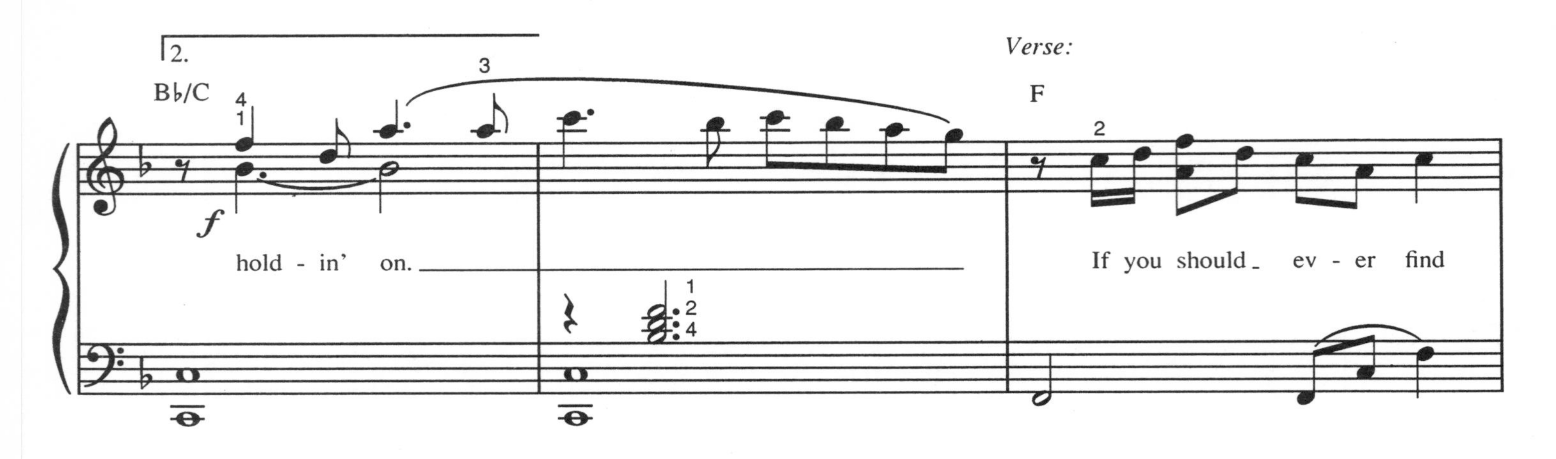
2.
Verse:
B♭/C
F
hold - in' on.
If you should ev - er find

C/E
Dm
Am
some - one new,
I know she'd bet - ter be
good to you.

B♭
Gm7
B♭/C
F
B♭/C
'Cause if she
does - n't then I'll be
there.
dim.
mp

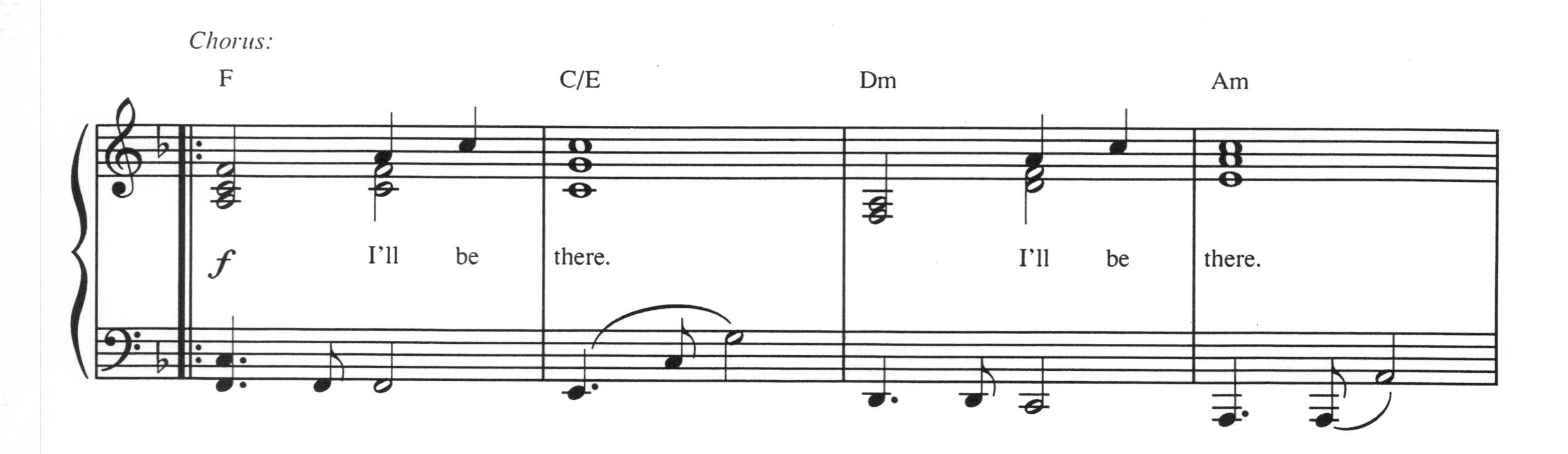
Chorus:
F
C/E
Dm
Am
I'll be
there.
I'll be
there.

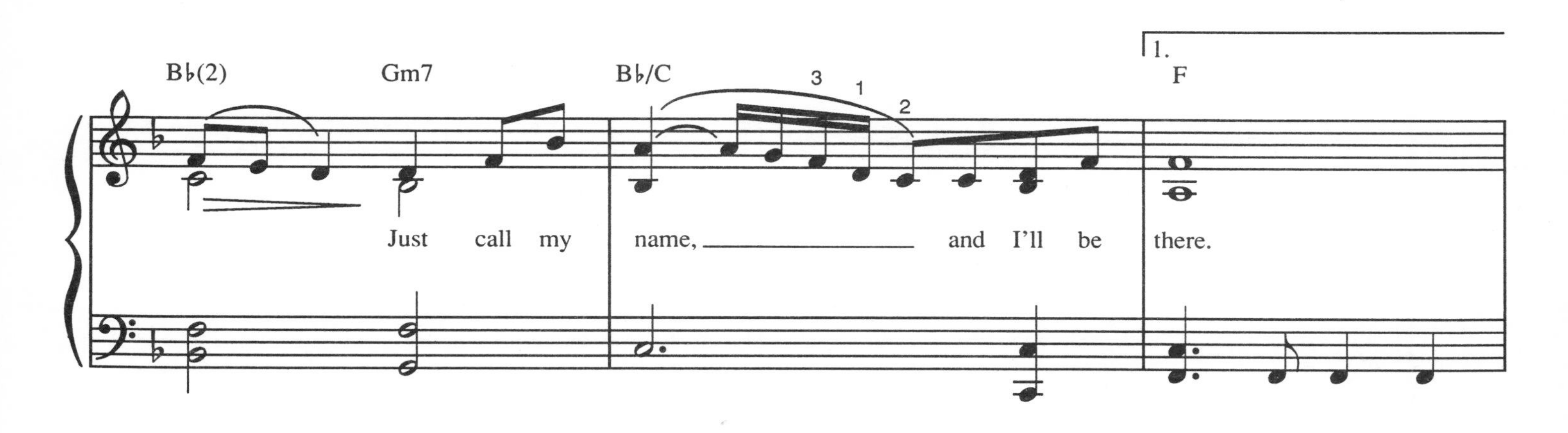
1.
B♭(2)
Gm7
B♭/C
F
Just call my name, and I'll be there.

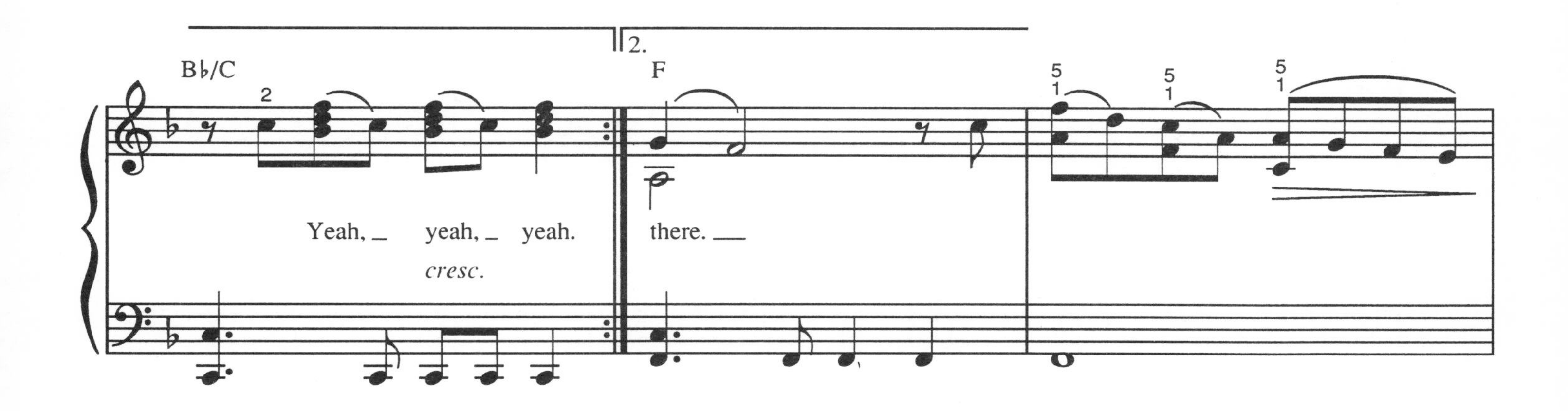
B♭/C
2.
F
Yeah, yeah, yeah.
cresc.
there.

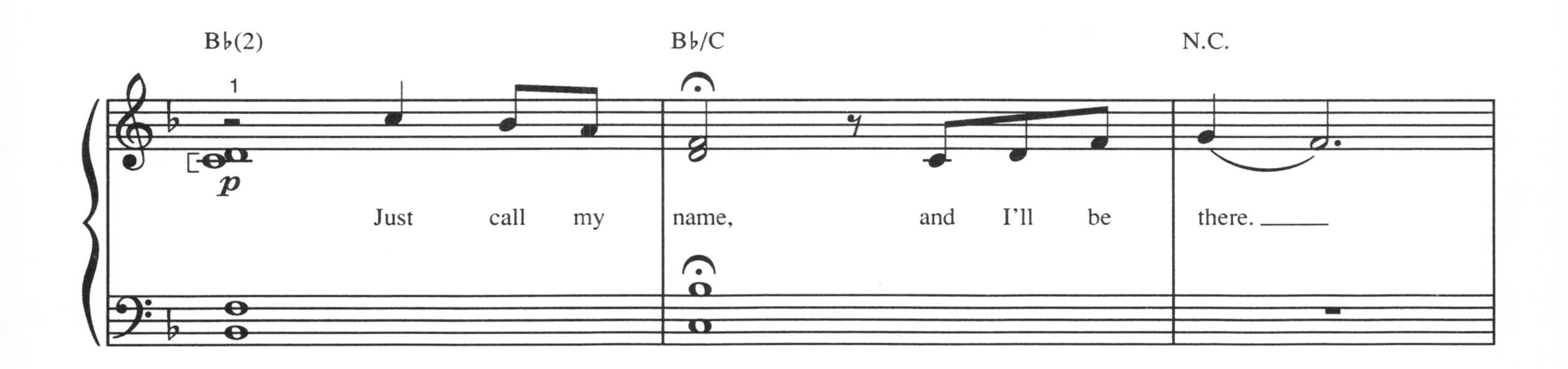
B♭(2)
B♭/C
N.C.
p
Just call my name, and I'll be there.

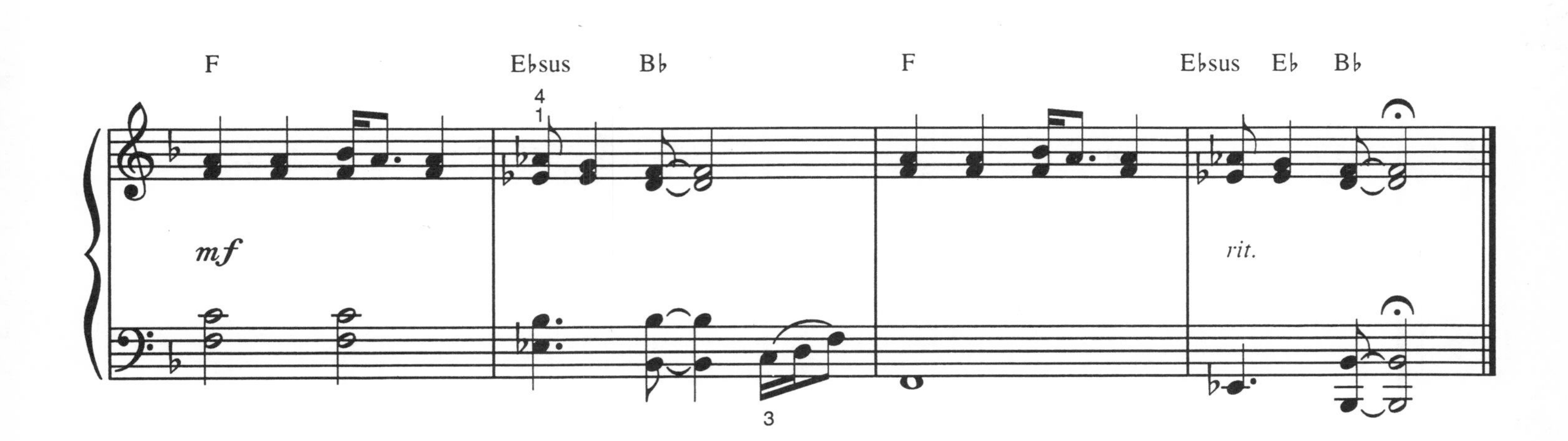
F
E♭sus
B♭
F
E♭sus
E♭
B♭
mf
rit.

I'M IN THE MOOD FOR LOVE

Words and Music by
JIMMY McHUGH and DOROTHY FIELDS

G
C
F6
G6
C/E
A7sus4
A7
I'm in the mood for love?
Why stop to think of whe-ther
mp
Fm6/A♭
G
C
Am6
B7
this lit - tle dream might fade?
We've put our hearts to -
Em
Am7♭5
D
Fm6/A♭
G7sus4
G7
- ge - ther, now we are one
I'm not a - fraid.
C
F6
Dm7
G
C
If there's a cloud a - bove,
mf
if it should rain we'll let it,
Em7
E♭dim
Dm7
G
C
but for to-night, for - get it,
I'm in the mood for love.

SAVING ALL MY LOVE FOR YOU

Words by GERRY GOFFIN
Music by MICHAEL MASSER

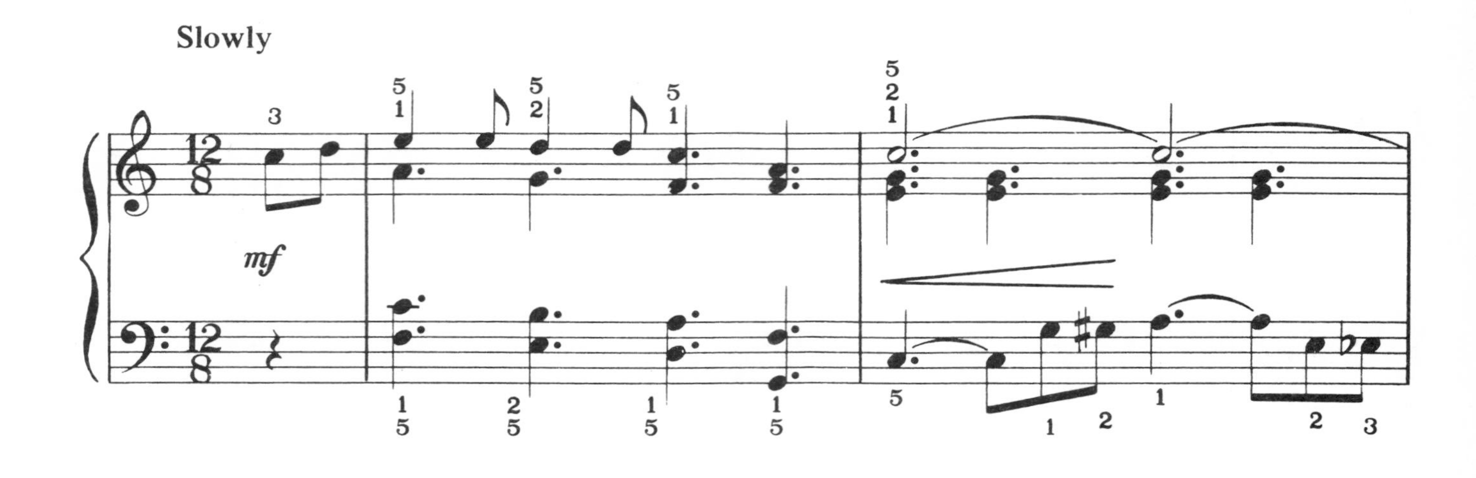

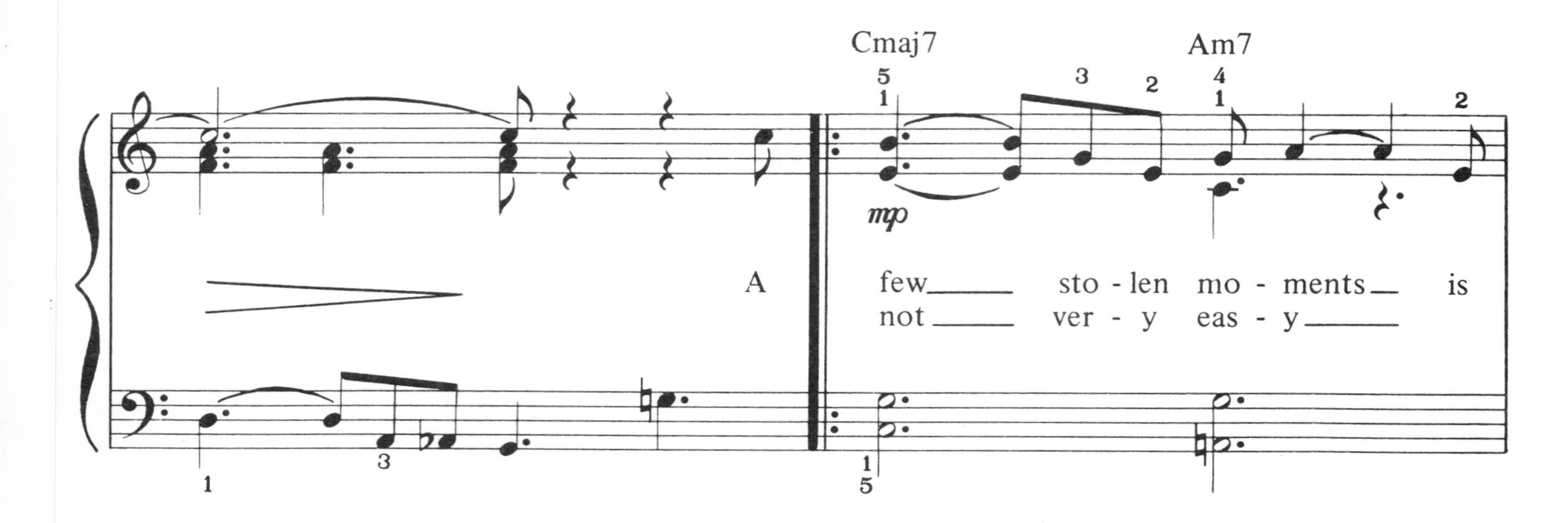

Dm7 F/G Am7 D/A
they need you there. Though I try to re - sist be - ing
man of my own. But each time I try, I just
Am7 D/A C Am7
last on your list, but no oth - er man's gon - na
break down and cry. 'Cause I'd rath - er be home feel - in'
Bm7 E7 Fmaj7 Em7 Dm7 F/G
do, so I'm sav - ing all my love for
blue,
mf
1. C Am7 Dm7 F/G 2. C
you. It's you.

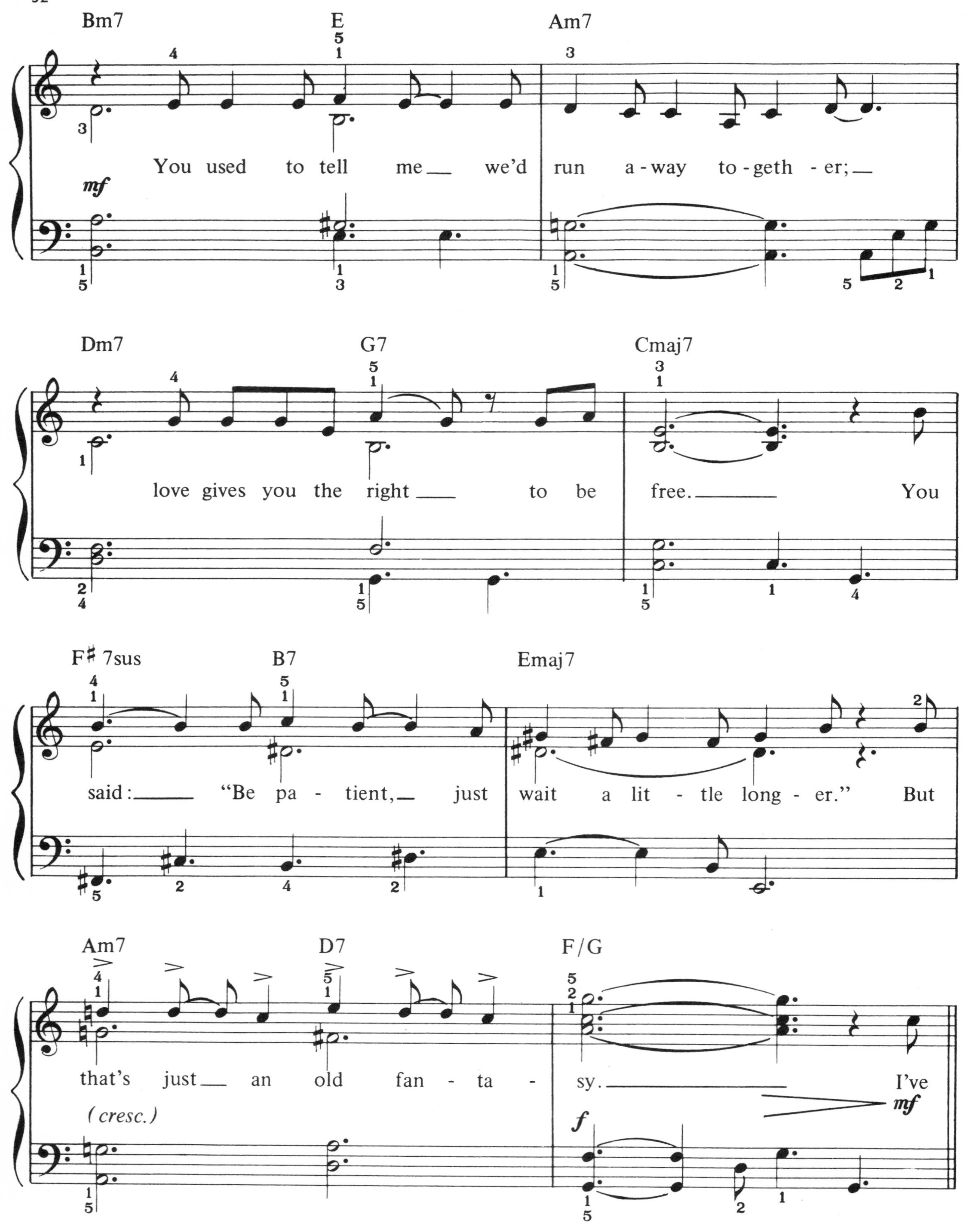
Bm7
E
Am7
You used to tell me we'd run a-way to-geth-er;
mf
Dm7
G7
Cmaj7
love gives you the right to be free. You
F♯ 7sus
B7
Emaj7
said: "Be pa-tient, just wait a lit-tle long-er." But
Am7
D7
F/G
that's just an old fan-ta-sy. I've
(cresc.)
f
mf

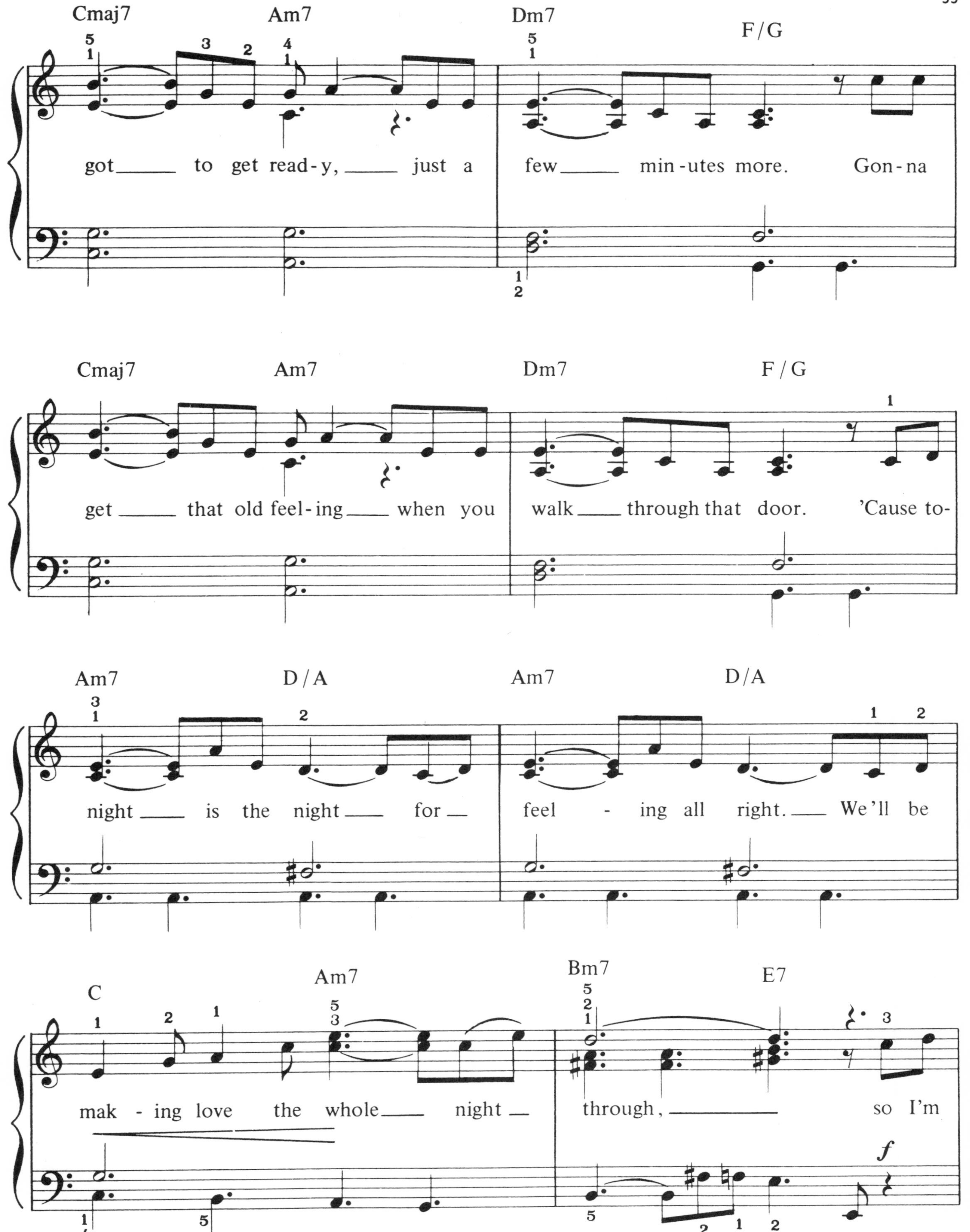
Cmaj7
Am7
Dm7
F/G
got to get read-y, just a
few min-utes more. Gon-na
get that old feel-ing when you
walk through that door. 'Cause to-
Am7
D/A
night is the night for
feel - ing all right. We'll be
C
Bm7
E7
mak - ing love the whole night
through, so I'm

Fmaj7 Em7 Dm7 Fmaj7 Em7 Dm7
sav - ing all my love, yes, I'm sav - ing all my love, yes, I'm
Fmaj7 Em7 Dm7 F/G C Am7
sav - ing all my love for you.
Dm7 F/G Cmaj7 Am7
No oth - er wom - an is
mf
Dm7 F/G Am7 D/A
gon - na love you more. 'Cause to - night is the night that I'm
(cresc.)

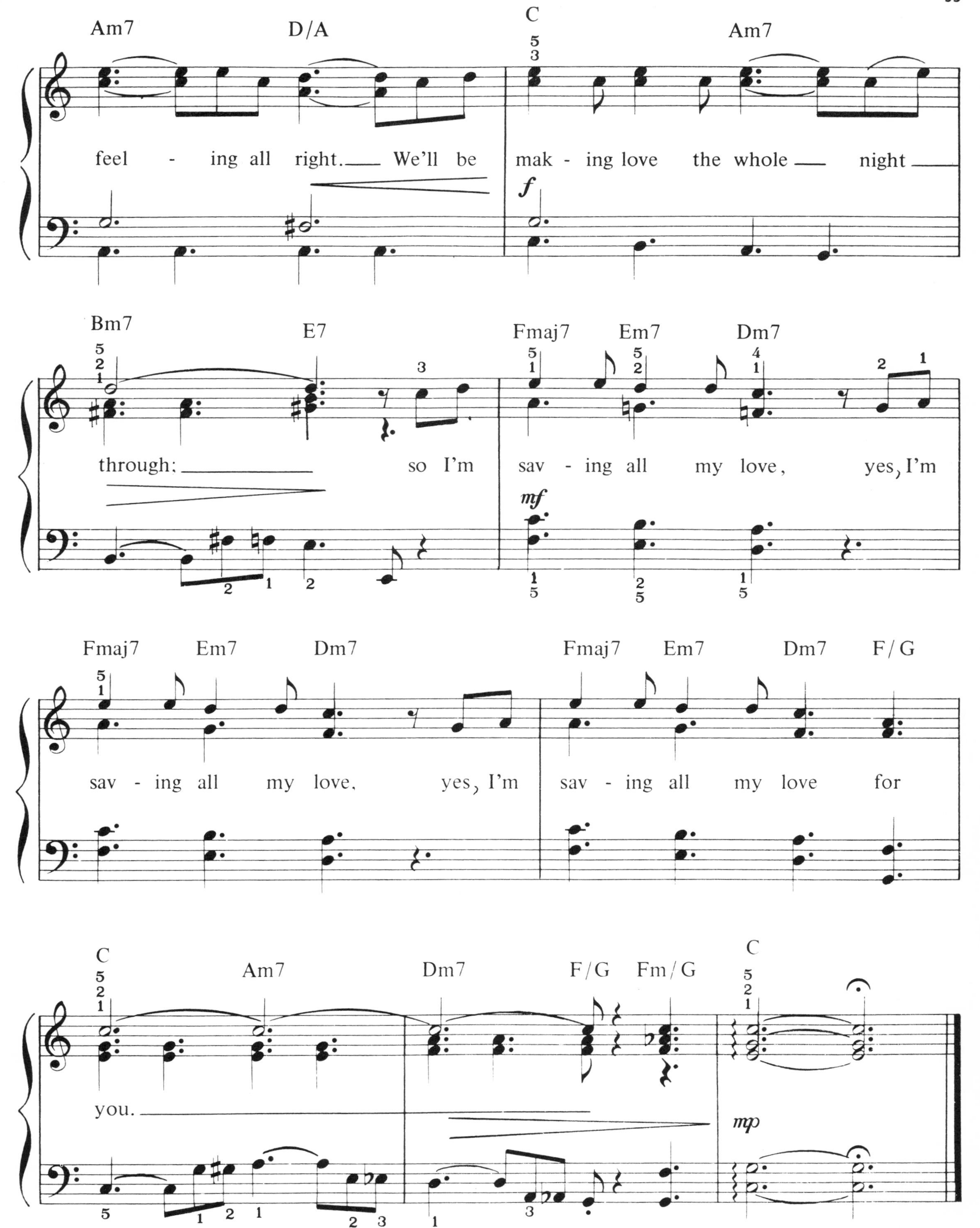
Am7 D/A C Am7
feel - ing all right. We'll be mak - ing love the whole night
f
Bm7 E7 Fmaj7 Em7 Dm7
through; so I'm sav - ing all my love, yes, I'm
mf
Fmaj7 Em7 Dm7 Fmaj7 Em7 Dm7 F/G
sav - ing all my love, yes, I'm sav - ing all my love for
C Am7 Dm7 F/G Fm/G C
you.
mp

WILL YOU LOVE ME TOMORROW?

Words and Music by
GERRY GOFFIN and CAROLE KING

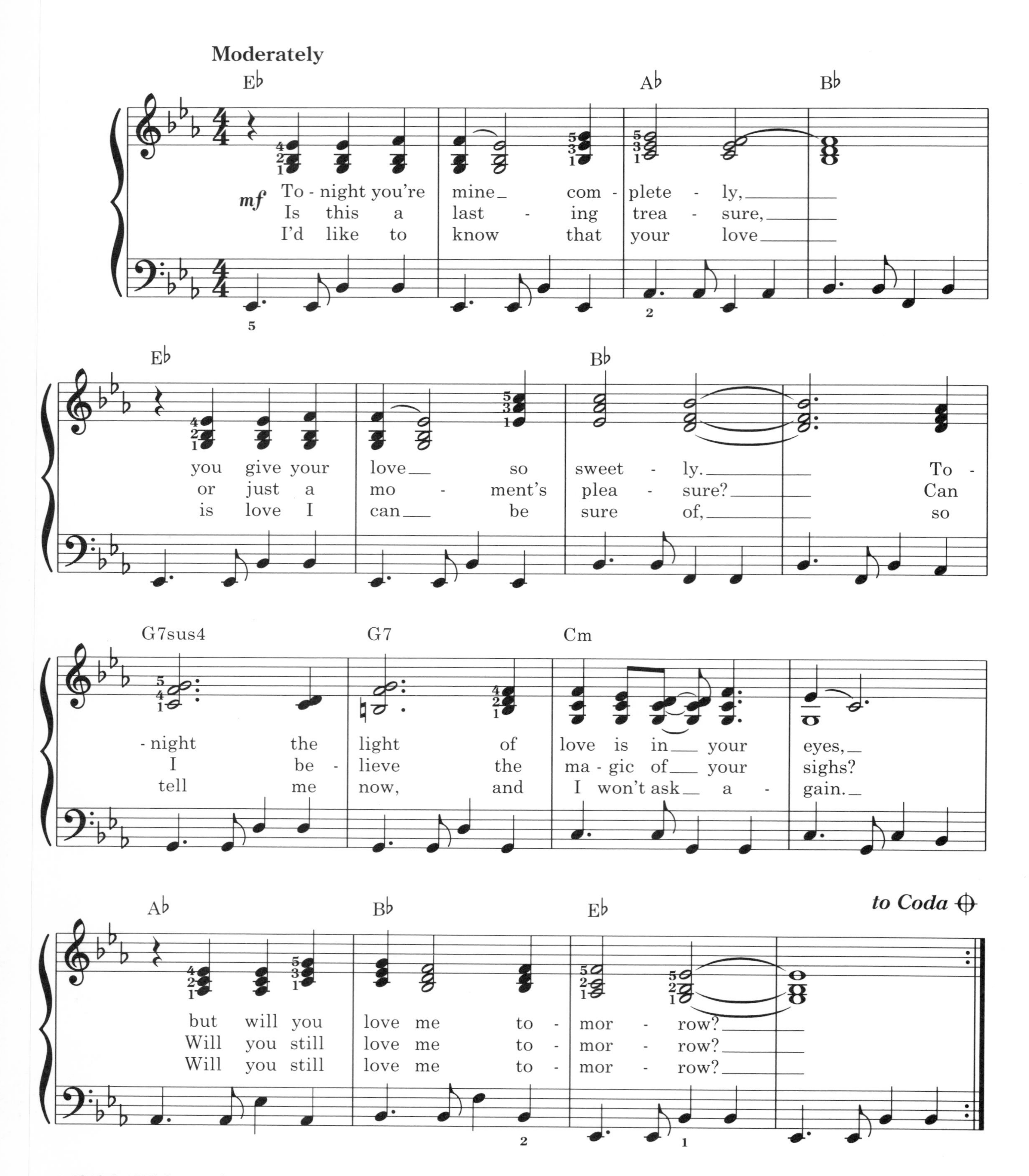

Ab
Gm
To - night with words un - spo - ken,
Ab
Eb
you say that I'm the on - ly one,
Ab
Gm
but will my heart be bro - ken when the
Cm
F
Bb11
Bb
D.C. al Coda
night meets the morn - ing sun?
CODA
Ab
Bb
Eb
Will you still love me to - mor - row?

YOU ARE SO BEAUTIFUL

Words and Music by
BILLY PRESTON and BRUCE FISHER

B♭
B♭maj7
A
you're ev - 'ry - thing that I hope for, and what's more,
cresc.
Dm
G9
Gm7♭5/B♭
F/C
Fmaj7/C F7/C
you're ev - 'ry - thing I need.
You are so
sub. p
1.
B♭
B♭m
F
B♭/F
F
B♭/C
C7
beau - ti - ful, ba - by, to me.
2.
B♭
B♭m
F
beau - ti - ful to me.
pp
8va

YOU NEEDED ME

Words and Music by
CHARLES R GOODRUM

C
A7
back for me, and held me up, and gave me
at the end, and turned my lies back in - to

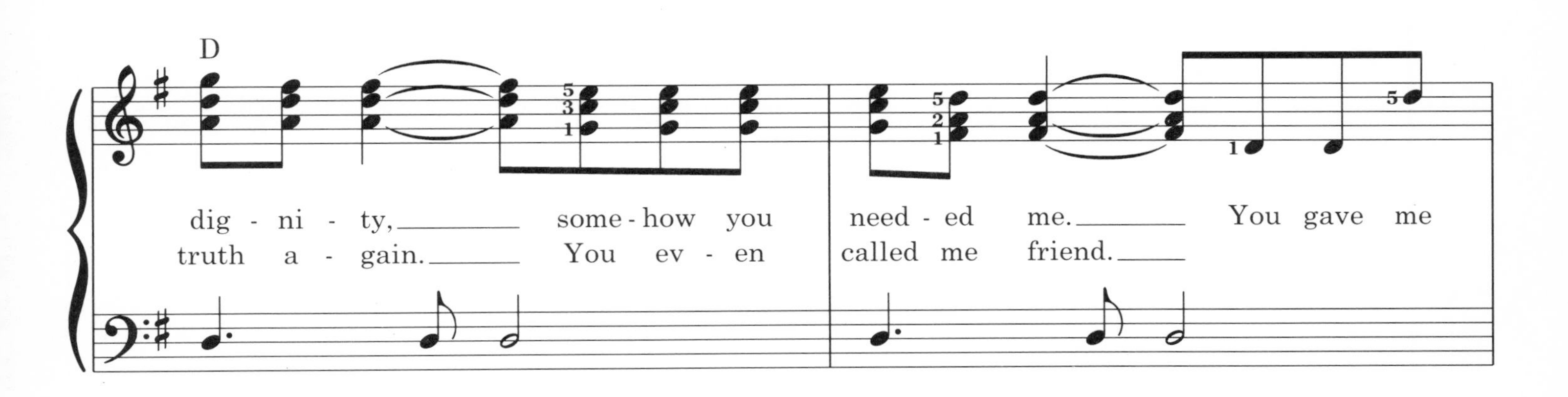
D
dig - ni - ty, some - how you need - ed me. You gave me
truth a - gain. You ev - en called me friend.

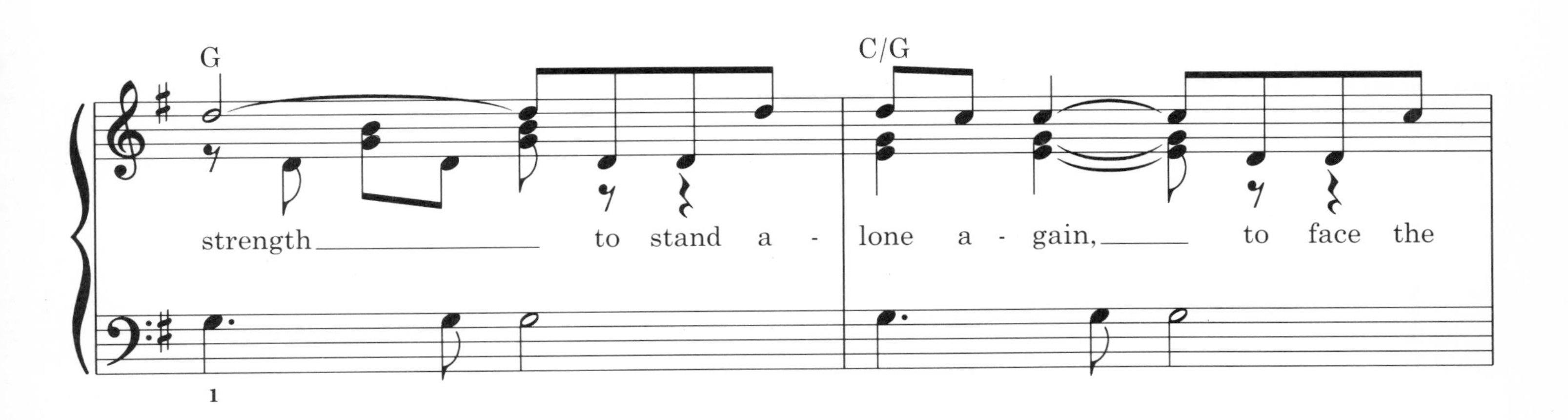
G
C/G
strength to stand a - lone a - gain, to face the

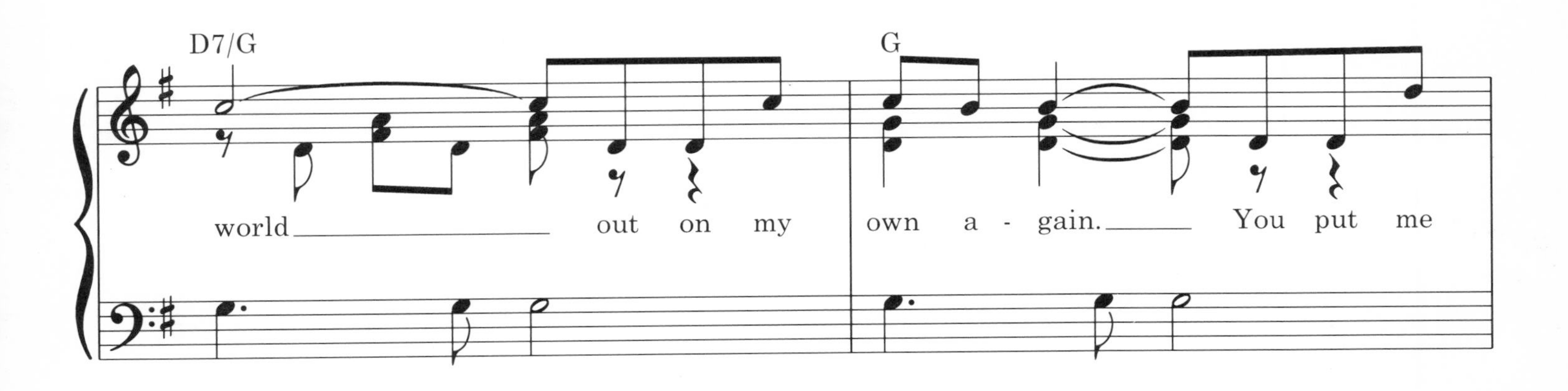
D7/G
G
world out on my own a - gain. You put me

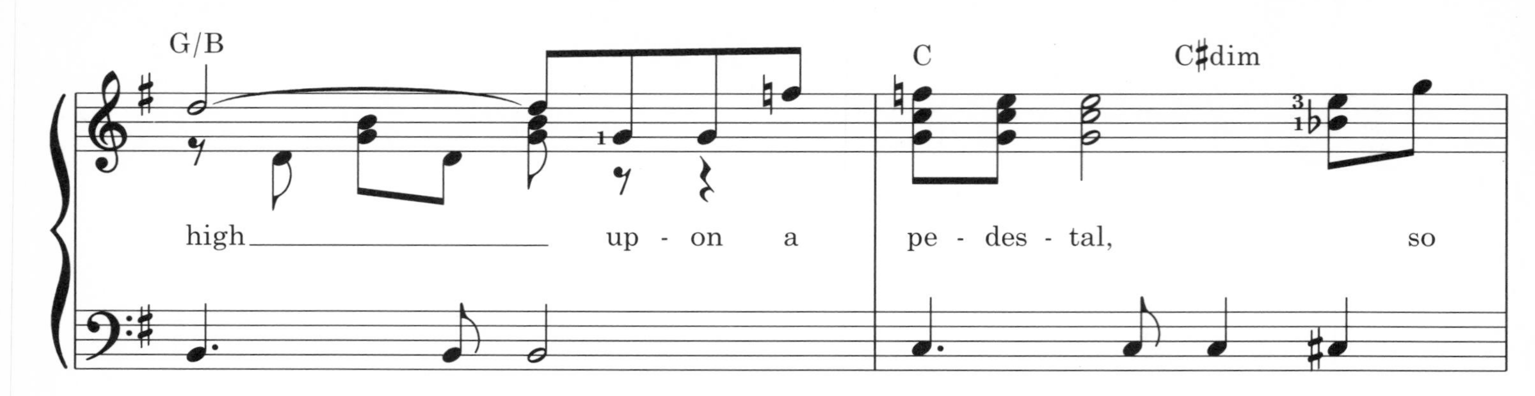
G/B
C
C♯dim
high upon a pe - des - tal, so

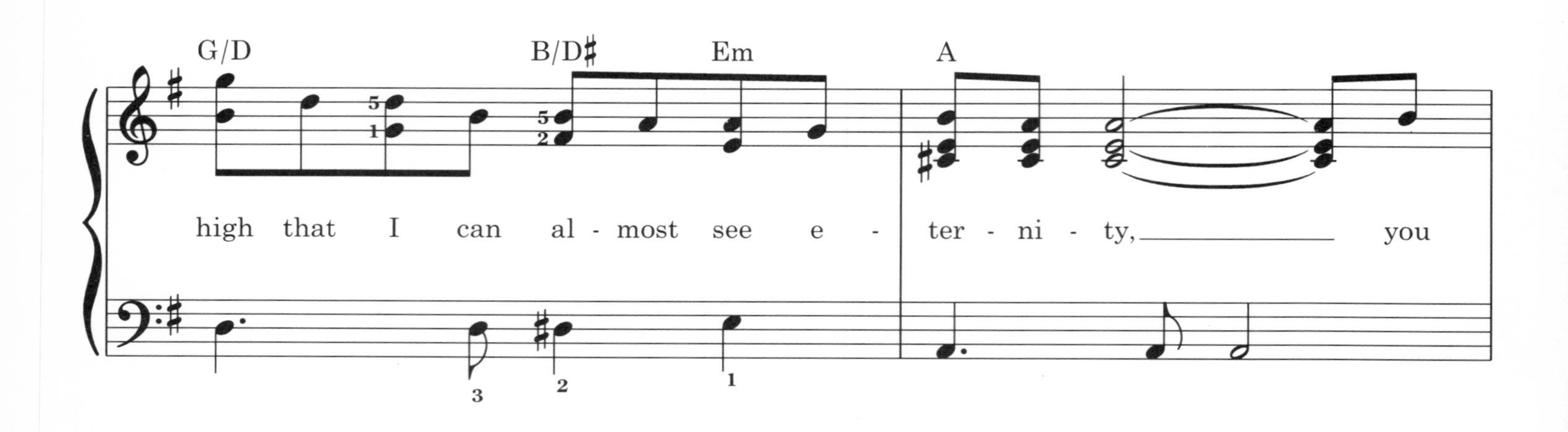
G/D
B/D♯
Em
A
high that I can al - most see e - ter - ni - ty, you

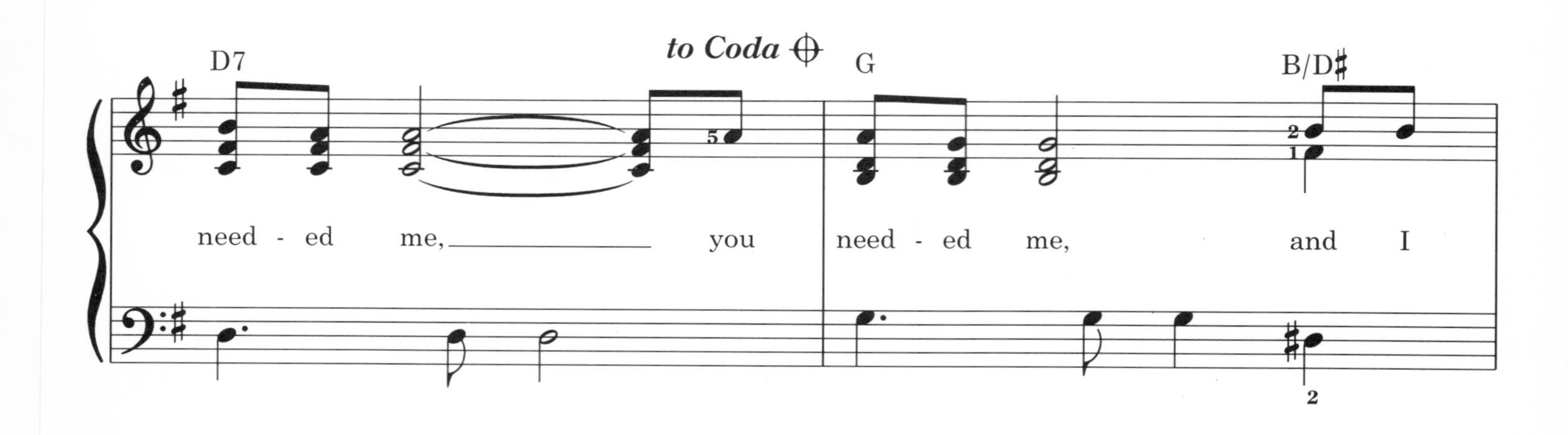
D7
to Coda
G
B/D♯
need - ed me, you need - ed me, and I

Em
G/D
C
G/B
can't be - lieve it's you, I can't be - lieve it's true. I

Am
C/D
G
B
need - ed you and you were
there,
and I'll

Em
G/D
C
G/B
ne - ver leave. Why should I leave? I'd
be a fool,
'cause I've

A7/C♯
A7
D7sus4
D
D.S. al Coda
fi - n'lly found some-one who real - ly
cares.
You held my

CODA
G
E7
A7
D7
G
need-ed me, you
need-ed me you
need-ed me.

THREE TIMES A LADY

Words and Music by
LIONEL RICHIE

G/F
Em7
B7+/D♯
come to the end of our rain - bow, there's
G
G/F
Em
some - thing I must say out loud.
B7+/D♯
pp
poco rit.
Chorus:
p
You're
G
once,
a tempo
D6/F♯
twice,
Bm7-5/F
three times a
C/E
la - dy,
Am
and I
G
love
D
D/C
you. Yes, you're
G
once,
D6/F♯
twice,

Verse 2:
You've shared my dreams, my joys, my pains;
You've made my life worth living for.
And if I had to live my life over again dear,
I'd spend every moment with you.
(To Chorus:)

Printed in England
The Panda Group · Haverhill · Suffolk · 7/97

also available in this series

Take it easy

LOVE SONGS

Always
Autumn Leaves (*Les Feuilles Mortes*)
Can't Stay Away From You
Close To You (They Long To Be)
Endless Love
The First Time Ever I Saw Your Face
Goodbye Girl
I'll Be There
I'm In The Mood For Love
The Power Of Love
Saving All My Love For You
Three Times A Lady
Will You Love Me Tomorrow?
You Are So Beautiful
You Needed Me

FILM CLASSICS

Eye Of The Tiger
Fame
Glory Of Love
I Have Nothing
It Must Have Been Love
(I've Had) The Time Of My Life
Philadelphia
Show Me Heaven
Take My Breath Away
Tears In Heaven
Theme From 'Superman'
Unchained Melody
Love Is In The Air

COUNTRY CLASSICS

Annie's Song
By The Time I Get To Phoenix
Constant Craving
Don't It Make My Brown Eyes Blue
Eagle When She Flies
Jolene
Lyin' Eyes
Outbound Plane
Standing Outside The Fire
Take It To The Limit
Take Me Home, Country Roads
Up On The Roof
Like A Sad Song

THE NINETIES

End Of The Road
Everybody's Talkin'
Get Here
Heal The World
Hero
I'll Stand By You
I Swear
A Million Love Songs
The Most Beautiful Girl In The World
Promise Me
Relight My Fire
Without You

CHILDREN'S TV FAVOURITES

The Banana Splits
Batman Theme
Blue Peter Theme (Barnacle Bill)
Hong Kong Phooey
The Magic Roundabout
(Meet) The Flintstones
Paddington Bear
Road Runner
Roobarb And Custard
Scooby Doo
Sesame Street
Thunderbirds
The Wombling Song
Yogi Bear
Postman Pat

SHOWTUNES

Another Openin', Another Show
Anything Goes
Cabaret
Edelweiss
Forty-Second Street
Getting To Know You
Hello Dolly
The Lady Is A Tramp
Let's Call The Whole Thing Off
This Can't Be Love
Thou Swell
True Love
Where Or When
With Every Breath I Take
If I Were a A Rich Man